THE SCRIPT

Published by
Wise Publications
14-15 Berners Street, London, W1T 3LJ, UK.

Exclusive distributors:
Music Sales Limited
Distribution Centre, Newmarket Road,
Bury St Edmunds, Suffolk, IP33 3YB, UK.

Music Sales Pty Limited
20 Resolution Drive, Caringbah, NSW 2229, Australia.

Order No. AM995962
ISBN 978-1-84772-826-5
This book © Copyright 2008 Wise Publications,
a division of Music Sales Limited.

Edited by Fiona Bolton.
Music arranged by Derek Jones & Jack Long.
Music processed by Paul Ewers Music Design.

Printed in the EU.

Wise Publications
part of The Music Sales Group
London/New York/Paris/Sydney/Copenhagen/Berlin/Madrid/Tokyo

WE CRY

Words & Music by Stephen Kipner, Mark Sheehan,
Daniel O'Donoghue & Glen Power

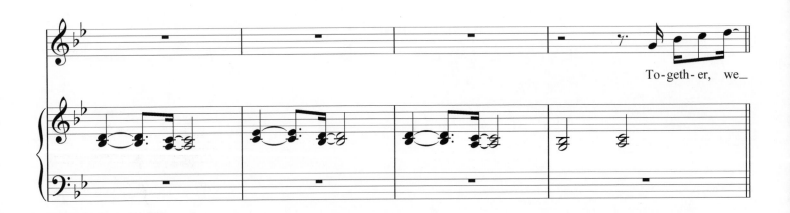

___ cry._____

2. What a-bout the John Play? Could have gone the whole way; light-ing up the
(Verse 3, see block lyrics)

stage try'n'- a get a deal.__Now he's light-ing up the wrong way, some-thing for the pain. Man, you wan-na see this

kid, he was so fuck-in' un - real. When he gets__ that call__ he's too__ far gone, can't

get it to-geth- er to sing__ one song._____ But they won't hear__ to-night__ the

D.S. al Coda

let-ter that they've gone to some-thing bet-ter. Bet you're sor-ry now, I won't be com-ing home to-night.

I'm sick of look-ing for those he-roes in the sky to teach us how to fly. To-geth-er, we cry. To-geth-er, we

Coda

Repeat and fade

To-geth-er, we____ cry._____ To-geth-er, we

Verse 3:
Oh, Mary's ambitious,
She wanna be a politician.
She's been dreaming about it since she was a girl.
She thought that she'd be the one who could change the world,
Always try'n'a to pave the way for women in a man's world.
But life happened, house, kids, two cars,
Husband hits the jar, cheques that don't go very far now.
Now she ain't making changes, she keeps her mind on her wages,
The only rattling cages are her own.

BEFORE THE WORST

Words & Music by Mark Sheehan,
Daniel O'Donoghue & Glen Power

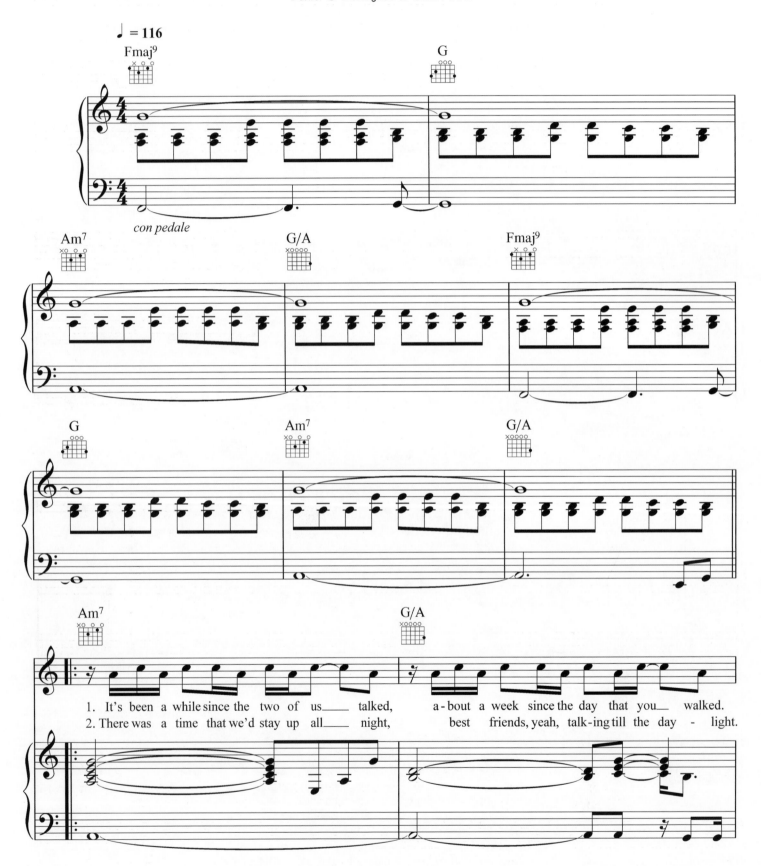

1. It's been a while since the two of us___ talked, a-bout a week since the day that you___ walked.
2. There was a time that we'd stay up all___ night, best friends, yeah, talk-ing till the day - light.

13

TALK YOU DOWN

Words & Music by Mark Sheehan & Daniel O'Donoghue

1. I can feel the col - our run - ning,
2. Grab you suit - case, call a tax - i, it's
3. Tak - ing short - cuts through the al - leys

as it's fad - ing from my face.
three a. m. now, where you gon - na go?
while you're rac - ing through my mind.

Try to speak but noth - ing's com - ing,
Gon - na stay with friends in Lon - don,
Cops can chase, but they won't catch me,

THE MAN WHO CAN'T BE MOVED

Words & Music by Andrew Frampton,
Steve Kipner, Mark Sheehan & Daniel O'Donoghue

see me wait-ing for you___ on the corn-er of the street.   So I'm not___ mov - ing.___

I'm not   mov - ing.___

I'm not   mov - ing.___   I'm not   mov - ing.___

22

BREAKEVEN

Words & Music by Andrew Frampton,
Stephen Kipner, Mark Sheehan & Daniel O'Donoghue

1. (𝄋) I'm still a-live but I'm bare - ly breath-ing...

Just prayed to a God that I don't be - lieve_ in._

'Cause I got time while she got free - dom._

To Coda ⊕

'Cause when a heart breaks, no, it don't break e - ven._

2. Her best days will be some of my_ worst._
(3.) say bad things hap-pen for a rea - son,_ but

28

RUSTY HALO

Words & Music by Mark Sheehan & Daniel O'Donoghue

run - ning from some - thing but we don't know when it's com - ing so we keep

run - ning and run - ning got - ta. Ev -'ry - one's run - ning from some - thing but we don't

know when it's com - ing so we keep run - ning and run - ning and run - ning. 1. Now I'm

look - ing at the Bi - ble, try'n'-a find a loop - hole.
(2.) run - ning for the light in the tun - nel, but it's just the train.

39

THE END WHERE I BEGIN

Words & Music by Mark Sheehan & Daniel O'Donoghue

1, 3. Some-times   tears_ say   all_
2. Some-times   we_ don't   learn_

_ there is   to   say._
_ from our mis-takes._

Some-times your first scars won't ev-er fade a-way.
Some-times we've no choice but to walk a-way, a-way.

Tried to break my heart; well, it's broke. Tried to hang

me high; well, I'm choked. Want-ed rain on me; well, I'm soaked,

soaked to the skin. It's the end where I be-gin.

To Coda

41

FALL FOR ANYTHING

Words & Music by Mark Sheehan & Daniel O'Donoghue

Original key B♭ minor

♩ = 122

Em   Am⁷

Girl, they'll bring you down, down, down.

N.C.

1. Don't give your-self a-way,   don't live your life that way;   of course he's gon-na say
2. Please don't be so na-ïve,   don't wait till your heart bleeds,   love was-n't built for speed,

an-y-thing you want, then leave quick-er than he came. Now you've got your-self to blame;   don't
lis-ten to me girl. He keeps fuck-in' with your head, try'n'-a get you in-to bed,   and

Am   Asus²

put your self back in the fire a-gain.   } It's the same damn things you're so
in the morn-ing you'll just hate your-self.

46

49

Girl, they'll bring you down, down,___ down.___

I'M YOURS

Words & Music by Daniel O'Donoghue

ANYBODY THERE

Words & Music by Mark Sheehan & Daniel O'Donoghue

58

Oh, I don't care,___'cause I won't know an-y-bod-y there._

Is there an - y - bod-y there?___ Is there an-y-bod-y there?_

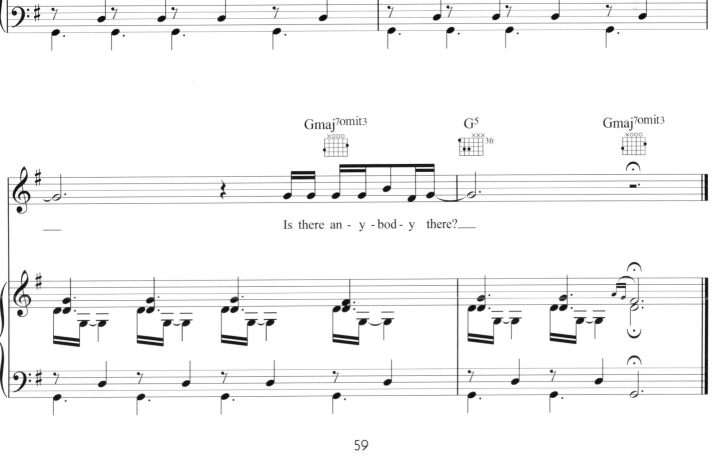

Is there an - y - bod- y there?___

IF YOU SEE KAY

Words & Music by Mark Sheehan,
Daniel O'Donoghue & Tony McGuinness

3456789